THE TEDDY BEAR SAY-A-PICTURE STORYBOOK

THE TEDDY BEAR SAY-A-PICTURE STORYBOOK

Illustrated by Jenny Tulip
Written by Zoe Antoniou

INDEX

First published by Ultimate Editions in 1996

© 1996 Anness Publishing Limited

Ultimate Editions is an imprint of
Anness Publishing Limited
Hermes House
88-89 Blackfriars Road
London SE1 8HA

ISBN 1 86035 194 8

Publisher Joanna Lorenz
Editor Zoe Antoniou
Designer Ian Sandom
Computer Assistance Andrew Marshall

Many thanks to Martin Lorenz and Michael Johnstone for their contributions.

Printed and bound in Hong Kong

THE TEDDY BEAR SAY-A-PICTURE STORYBOOK

Contents

 Teddy Bear at Home 7

Teddy Bear at the Farm 29

 Teddy Bear at School 51

Teddy Bear on Holiday 73

TEDDY BEAR'S HOUSE

Teddy Bear's house

Oh, look at that ,
With a door open wide.
Let's move a bit nearer,
And see what's inside.

There's a hat and a bag,
That belong to a teddy.
Let's knock on the door,
To make sure he's there.

In the hall

Here is the hall,
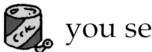 you see Ted Bear?
He takes a ,
And hangs his 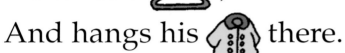 there.

He takes off his ,
It's put on a peg.
He tugs on each ,
Pulls one off each .

10

But as he bends down,
The  then runs by.
She's chased by the  ,
How quickly they fly!

They  down poor Bear,
As they push through the door.
"Oh  , what a bump!"
He says, shaking his  .

11

In the kitchen

In Teddy's kitchen,
What can you see?
There's  and there's  ,
And a hot  of tea.

If you are hungry,
There's  and some  .
There are  and  ,
Some  and  .

12

The  tin's empty,
So Bear starts to cook.
With 🥚, flour and 🧈,
How tasty it looks.

In a big 🥣,
Bear's making a 🍰.
He adds lots of 🥣,
And it's ready to bake.

13

In the dining room

Here is the dining room,
A big  is ready.
There's a 🥄 and a ⬤ ,
On the 🪑 for Teddy.

I see some 🎈🎈,
Some 🎀 and 🎉 .
Looks like a party,
How about that?

14

Here are Bear's friends,
Eating lots of fun things.
There's  ,  ,
And small  wings.

The cake has a  ,
They all have a  .
Some  is playing.
The food is so nice.

In the playroom

Here is the playroom,
Bear's favourite place,
With a  and a ,
And for his .

Can you see a ,
A and a ?
There's even a ,
Yes, there's something for all.

16

Ted puts on his ,
How quickly he  .
But soon he falls down,
When his  unties.

Now Bear  down,
And wants to play more.
He quickly completes,
A pretty  .

In the bathroom

Here in the bathroom,
Bear has a scrub.
He plays with his 🦆,
While he's in the .

He puts on his ,
Underwater he goes.
He blows some big ,
From the tip of his .

He then takes a ,
And dries in great haste.
He his ,
With some stripy .

19

In the living room

In the living room,

There's many more things.

A  and a ,

A that sings.

Bear sits on the ,

What can he see?

The cartoon, " ",

Is on the .

20

Now Bear cuts out ,
uts them in a pile.
He joins them together,
o make a .

Bear then takes some ,
And colouring ,
And draws lots of ,
Some fields and .

21

In the garage

In Teddy Bear's garage,
There is an old .
Its back is missing,
It will not go far.

In the of the car,
Is Teddy's.
But a and,
Still can't fix it.

There's various ,
With ██ and old ██,
With ██ Teddy Bear,
Can make some play things.

When the ☼ is out,
Bear takes his ██,
And he cycles around,
Wherever he likes.

23

In the garden

Let's go to the garden,
And see what is growing.
There are  and ,
And that needs mowing.

Teddy takes his ,
And pulls up the .
Soon he can start,
To all his .

24

Bear then goes around,

With his  .

When the 🌸 got wet,

How the 🐜 ran!

Now Teddy Bear sits,

In his garden 🪑 .

He soon falls 😴 ,

Without a worry or care.

25

In the bedroom

Bear puts on ,

And climbs into .

He won't go to sleep,

Till his  is all read.

He takes off his ,

Before he sleeps,

With lots of ,

And Teddy Bear sheets.

ometimes he'll have,

As a special treat,

A 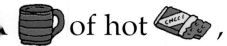 of hot chocolate,

Which warms his cold feet.

He turns off the lamp,

And closes his eyes.

He's dreaming of rainbows,

High up in the skies.

TEDDY BEAR
AT THE FARM

At the farmhouse

Here's an old farmhouse,

With a squeaky old  .

 leaves the  ,

As the  inside roars.

There's copper  hanging,

By the fireplace.

There's  and a poker,

And  of lace.

he  crows out loud,
nd wakes Bear at dawn.
e opens his 👀,
as a stretch and a 🐻.

Bear's here to help out,
He'll have to work hard.
Wearing work 👢👢 and 🧤🧤,
He goes into the yard.

In the stables

Bear first wakes the ,
From their deep sleep.
He picks up his ,
And then starts to sweep.

Ted brushes their ,
And their long manes.
He gives them a sugar ,
And puts on their .

he farmer gives them , They go to the blacksmith,

nd big piles of hay. Who moulds some .

ome flick a long , Then using some ,

nd let out a "Neigh!" They're fixed to the .

33

In the pig-sty

The home of the  ,
Is called a pig-sty.
They ♥ lots of mud,
Bear's not quite sure why.

They have small tails,
And trotters for .
They're and they're fat,
Since they love to eat.

34

ome pigs are ,
ome pigs are  .
he piglets squeak, "Oink!"
or some milk to drink.

Ted washes the floor,
With a  and  .
It's now feeding time,
He  them some slop.

35

In the henhouse

Bear's at the henhouse,
To visit the .
He's collecting their,
From the in the.

Ted lays down some,
And tidies their home.
They drop their brown,
Wherever they roam.

Cluck, cluck!" say the hens,
s they hop all around.
hey have two large wings,
ut can't  from the ground.

The   are bright yellow,
They follow their mums.
All the birds peck,
With their  for .

37

In the dairy

Look at the ,
They're black and they're white.
They chew lots of ,
All day and all night.

Bear goes to the dairy,
With his milking pail.
He sits on a ,
Next to the cow's .

Out comes the warm ,
As he pulls on her ⬤.
"Moo!" lows the cow,
And Bear jumps off his seat.

The milk is then cooled,
And mixed in some ⬤.
It makes ⬤ and ⬤,
Which is nice with bread rolls.

39

In the barn

Bear's in the old barn,
With piles of -stacks.
He uses his hay,
To put it in sacks.

High up in the rafters,
Are lots of nests.
There are in the corners,
With at rest.

40

here in the barn,
also a  .
ith his [bed] and his [pillow],
e's made a small house.

And in the dark night,
[owl] opens his eyes.
The [moon] shines above.
"Hoot! Hoot!" go his cries.

In the fields

The hillside looks golden,

With fields of crops.

The 👤👤 of corn 🤚 ,

As the wind strokes their tops.

Ted gets in his 🚜 ,

To harvest some wheat.

A 🧍 is there,

So the 🐦 can't eat.

he crops become flour,
t the .
s spin round,
igh up on the hill.

Some flour is white,
And some is .
It goes in big ,
To the market in town.

43

By the pond

Bear's by the ,
With birds everywhere.
There are in small groups,
And two geese in a .

Look at the white ,
With a neck that's so long.
She's the of the lake,
With wings big and strong.

44

order to paddle,

he ducks have webbed .

hey're dipping their heads,

catch  to eat.

On a ,

Sits a green .

He jumps with a ,

To a long floating .

45

On the hills

The  on the hill,
Are white with ❋ feet.
They stand around eating,
"Baa! Baa!" they all bleat.

Once every year,
Their 🧥 are sheared off.
The 🧶 is then knitted,
And made into cloth.

46

hep the sheep ,

eeps each  away.

ear has to ,

show him the way.

Out on the fields,

There are also some  .

They have beards and ,

And chew on Bear's coat.

47

In the orchard

Bear's in the orchard,
There are so many .
On some there are apples,
And others, red .

He puts in his ,
Some lovely green .
There are even some vines,
With  everywhere.

Bear climbs a  tree,

He's up very high.

He has an idea!

"Why, I'll make a big ."

Bear's work is now over,

He  to get clean.

He puts up his feet,

And has pie with .

TEDDY BEAR AT SCHOOL

Going to school

It's Monday morning,
Bear has to get up.
He eats  and ,
And drinks milk from a .

When the clock strikes ,
Bear's at the school ,
With his and his .
He is glad he's not late.

His  and tracksuit,
Are all in their place.
He's also packed up,
His long ✏️ – 🟫 .

Bear sits at his 🪑 ,
The teacher calls "Bear".
His name gets a ✔️ ,
When his 🖐️'s in the air.

In the classroom

There is a large ,
On the classroom wall,
A with ,
For teaching them all.

Around the classroom,
There are and ,
A and a .
What fun it all looks!

54

here's Ben the pet ,

ho's ever so nice.

here's Larry and Jerry,

ho are the school .

There are things from the park,

The children collected:

 and pressed ,

And they selected.

55

Playing with words

The lesson begins,
With and words.
A is for 🌰 ,
And B is for 🐤 .

What letter is next?
C can be a 🐱 .
Z ends the alphabet,
🦓 starts with that.

56

f you take some  T ,

And add it to 🧥 ,

t makes a new word.

They make a 👕 !

If you take a 🐝 ,

And the number 4 ,

"Before" is then made.

Do you know any more?

Using numbers

It's time for  1234 .
First, Ted must add up.
1 🟠 plus 2,
Makes 3 to eat up.

But if there's 5 🍬🍬 ,
And Ted eats up 2.
That 🍃⭐ just the 3,
Which is only a few.

Take 2  ,

X them by 3.

That makes 6 in total,

or U and for me.

Imagine 10 ✿✿ ,

Grouped in sets of 2.

They make up five 👜👜.

That's division for you!

Lunchtime

Now it's  ,

And Bear wants his lunch.

He opens his ,

And then starts to munch.

In his lunch ,

What else can you see?

A big – ,

For a hungry Teddy.

s well as all that,

here's a  – roll.

ar opens his ,

nd he swallows it whole.

Now he is thirsty,

He wants a cold .

He finishes lunch,

With cold water from the .

61

Art class

Bear likes to ,
All kinds of things.
A 🏠 or a 🦁,
Or maybe some 👑👑.

Today he is drawing,
A scene at the zoo,
With a 🦒 and 🐒,
And a large 🦘.

Using his ✂,
He cuts a ▲.
He makes some nice shapes;
A ■ and ▬.

Ted makes 🐸🐸 and 🐟,
Using some clay.
They go in the oven,
To cook on a ▱.

63

Playing music

Here is the music room,
With musical things.
The  is playing,
And everyone .

What instruments,
Can you see around?
A , a ;
make a big sound.

64

ed plays a △ ,

lis friend a ⌐ .

he teacher with ╱ ,

eeps the beat in order.

Some of the children,

Shake a ◎ .

Others clap 🖐🖐 ,

They make a great team.

Playtime

Now it's playtime,
Ted Bear runs outside.
Some  do a ,
Some play seek and hide.

Bear climbs up a ,
And shoots down the .
The ,
Is dizzy to ride.

Bear kicks his  – ⚽ ,
And scores a great 🥅 .
He chases it round,
But how fast it rolls!

Bear sits on a 🎠 .
How high he can 🪰 ,
Backwards and forwards,
Up into the sky.

Storytime

At the end of the day,
A story is .
The children all sit,
On , cross-legged.

The is reading,
A nursery rhyme.
C if you know it,
And follow each line.

Little Jack Horner,

at in the corner,

ating his Christmas  .

"He put in his  ,

And pulled out a  ,

And said,

'What a good boy am  !' "

Hometime

The day is over,
When the  rings.
Bear jumps from his ,
You'd think he had wings.

He runs through the ,
And there is Ted's mum,
While waiting at home,
Is a nice cream .

ed's in the garden,

nd so  his friends.

hey run all around,

o he's tired when it ends.

Soon it's suppertime,

And then time for 🛏️.

What a busy day!

🍬 dreams to you, Ted.

TEDDY BEAR ON HOLIDAY

Packing the suitcase

Bear's getting ready,
It's holiday time.
He's off to the  ,
Where there's  and  .

He's taking some  ,
A  , a  ,
And must not forget,
His  .

The  is now full,
The won't close,
With four pairs of ,
And too many clothes.

There are thick, woolly ,
A , pyjamas,
– not the right things,
When you're in the Bahamas.

75

On the aeroplane

Bear picks up his 🎫,
Locks up with his 🔑.
He's off to the 🏢,
Inside a 🚗.

He sits in his 🛋️,
And fastens his 🔗.
The ✈️ soon takes off,
How dizzy he felt.

High up in the ,
The 🌍 looks so small.
There's a big 🪂,
In case they should fall.

They fly over ⛰,
That are so far down.
Look, there's a 🗺,
And a large 🏢.

At the hotel

Soon Bear has arrived,
He's at the hotel.
He walks to the  ,
And 🔔 the desk 🔔 .

He goes up the 📶 ,
To room 302.
He looks through the 🪟 ,
What a nice view!

78

e runs to the ,

nd straight inside.

hen lies on a ,

njoying the ride.

Just look at Ted Bear,

Under the .

He sips juice,

And is eating paella.

79

At the seaside

Bear's taking a ,
He's off to the sea.
He wears his ,
Since it's so sunny.

His is full,
With his and mat.
He sits on a ,
And puts on his .

80

e pours on ,

nd lies in the sun.

he "🧤"lap his 🐾,

h, he's having such fun.

Bear now feels thirsty,

He buys an 🍦.

It melts down his 🐻,

– he can 🦫 to get clean.

In the sea

Bear wears his ,
And goes for a swim.
Look, there's a ,
A and .

He then sees a coral,
On the seabed;
A and ,
That are and .

82

Bear's now at the rockpool,

There are urchins and .

But the pool is too small,

For big  and .

Bear takes his ,

He surfs on the waves.

He then goes exploring,

In old s' caves.

On the beach

Bear makes a  ,
And digs with his .
Using his ,
The turrets are made.

He makes a big ,
With different-shaped .
There's for hair.
Pooh! How funny it smells.

84

ear rides a  ,

e sits in the ⚱ .

When he gets hot,

e goes for a paddle.

85

Beach games

Now Bear wants to play,
With his  and  .
But just as he swings,
His  hits the wall.

Look, there are  ,
Playing volley-ball.
Poor Bear hits the  ,
He's really too small.

ear gets in a ,

nd tries hard to row.

it he loses an ,

nd soon needs a .

He'll try one more sport,

He's off water – .

He holds the tight,

How fast he is speeding!

At the fairground

Bear's at the fairground,
How happy he feels.
He likes the  – ,
And huge Ferris .

He sits on a ,
On the merry-go-round.
The ,
Takes him far from the groun

e buys ,

nd a big toffee ,

e plays spin the ,

nd wins a .

It's bumper time.

His foot's on the pedal.

He's doing so ,

He gets given a .

89

At the circus

Bear's gone to the ,
Oh, look there's a .
He tries to spin ,
But trips and falls down.

His friend juggles ,
They fly everywhere.
He stands on his ,
But his tear.

90

he trapeze artist,
up on his  .
 dances,
nd a starts to sing.

See the magician,
With his black .
He pulls out a ,
And then a white .

Going home

Bear writes lots of  ,
To family and friends.
He takes some good ,
Through his lens.

He now must go shopping,
For and .
There are shell-covered ,
And other nice treats.

92

He's so sad to go,

Bear sheds a .

It would great,

To come back next year.

GOODBYE!